How to use this book

Follow the advice, in italics, given for you on each page.
Praise *the children at every step!*

Detailed guidance is provided in the Read Write Inc. Phonics Handbook.

7 reading activities

Children:

☆ *Practise reading the speed sounds.*

☆ *Read the green and red words for the Ditty.*

☆ *Listen as you read the introduction.*

☆ *Read the Ditty.*

☆ *Re-read the Ditty and discuss the 'questions to talk about'.*

☆ *Re-read the Ditty with fluency and expression.*

☆ *Practise reading the speed words.*

Speed Sounds

Consonants

Say the pure sounds (do not add 'uh').

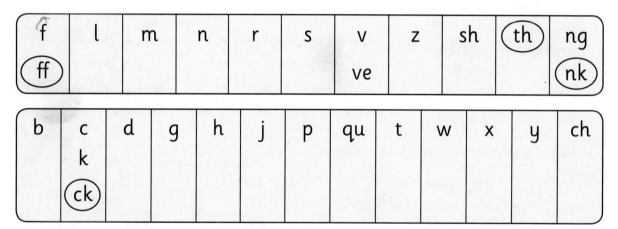

f	l	m	n	r	s	v	z	sh	(th)	ng
(ff)						ve				(nk)

b	c	d	g	h	j	p	qu	t	w	x	y	ch
	k											
	(ck)											

Vowels

Say the sounds in and out of order.

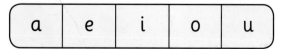

a	e	i	o	u

Each box contains only one sound. Focus sounds are circled.

Ditty 1 Wuff wuff

Green words

Read in Fred Talk (pure sounds).

got   fat   dog   big   wuff

thin   a   black   and   has

Read the root word first and then with the ending.

pup → pups

Red words

my

Wuff wuff

Introduction

In this story we meet a dog and her pups. Let's see what they are like!

my dog has got 4 pups

a big pup ...

a bla<u>ck</u> pup...

a <u>th</u>in pup...

and a fat pup

wu<u>ff</u> wu<u>ff</u>

Ditty 2 Help

Read in Fred Talk (pure sounds).

nap sit nip on sand

a p<u>i</u>nk help ha<u>ve</u> soft

<u>qu</u>i<u>ck</u> flat crab

Red words

I <u>the</u>

7

Ditty 2 Help

Introduction

Do you like going to the beach? The girl in this story has fun at the beach, but then she has a surprise...

I sit on <u>the</u> soft sand

I ha<u>ve</u> a <u>qu</u>i<u>ck</u> nap

nip nip

a flat pi<u>nk</u> crab

help help

Ditty 3 # The big match

Green words

Read in Fred Talk (pure sounds).

win big net man ki<u>ck</u>

ba<u>ck</u> clap in a it is

Read the root word first and then with the ending.

red → reds

Red words

<u>th</u>e of

Ditty 3   The big match

Introduction
This is a story about a game of football. Can the red team win?

a man...

a big ki<u>ck</u>...

it is in <u>the</u> ba<u>ck</u> of <u>the</u> net

clap clap clap

<u>th</u>e reds win

Questions to talk about

Ditty 1

How many pups does the dog have?

What do the pups look like?

Tell me about a dog you know.

Ditty 2

What does the girl do after sitting on the sand?

What happens to the girl whilst she is napping?

What do you like doing at the seaside?

Ditty 3

What happens when the man kicks the ball?

Which team wins?

What is your favourite game?

Speed words for Ditty 1

Children practise reading the words across the rows, down the columns and in and out of order clearly and quickly.

got	fat	my	thin
big	dog	a	black

Speed words for Ditty 2

have	crab	sand	flat
pink	help	sit	soft

Speed words for Ditty 3

win	big	in	the	net
clap	kick	back	a	man